The Young Experimenters' Workbook

Treasures of the Earth

by Harry and Laura Sootin

illustrated by Frank Aloise

W · W · Norton & Company · Inc · New York

Contents

Introduction

Men need things from the earth. They take sand from the top of the ground. They pry up big rocks. They dig deep to find metals like gold and copper and iron.

Sand is used to make concrete and glass. Rocks are cut into blocks for buildings. Metals from the ground become bridges, and railroads, and money.

Scientists look in the earth to find things that men can use. You can study the earth like a scientist by doing the experiments in this book.

Hardness

You can begin your experiments with the minerals in your home. Scientists have discovered that some minerals are harder than others. The test for hardness helps us find out what minerals a rock has in it. It also makes it easier to tell one mineral from another.

You can find out the hardness of a mineral by giving it the scratch test. Every kind of mineral can be given a number that tells how hard it is. Diamond, the hardest mineral, is number 10. Talc, the softest mineral, is number 1. A mineral will scratch anything as hard as or softer than itself. It can be scratched by anything as hard as or harder than itself.

Here is the scientist's hardness chart:

1	talc
2	gypsum
3	calcite
4	fluorite
5	apatite
6	feldspar
7	quartz
8	topaz
9	corundum
10	diamond

Here is a hardness chart made of things you can find:

1	soft lead pencil point
1½	ice near freezing temperature
2	blackboard chalk
2½	fingernail
2½–3	silver
3	copper penny
4	yellow brass
5	nail file
5½	knife blade; bottle glass
6½	steel file
7	flint (quartz) sandpaper
7½	garnet paper
9	emery paper
9½	carborundum or silicon carbide paper

Hardness Tests

The softest minerals are talc and graphite. Both have Hardness 1 (H1). Your fingernail has Hardness 2½ (H2½), so it leaves a scratch or groove on softer substances.

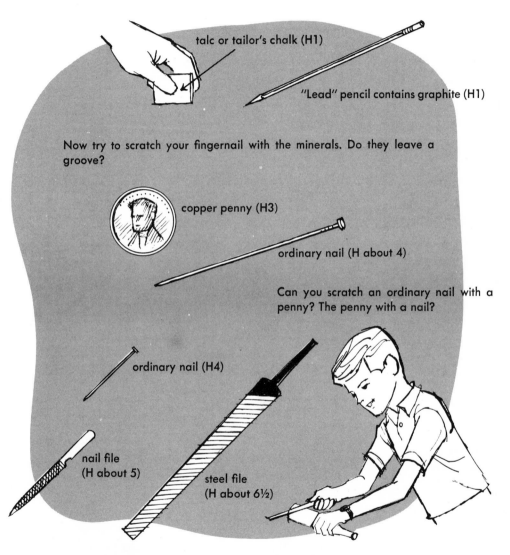

talc or tailor's chalk (H1)

"Lead" pencil contains graphite (H1)

Now try to scratch your fingernail with the minerals. Do they leave a groove?

copper penny (H3)

ordinary nail (H about 4)

Can you scratch an ordinary nail with a penny? The penny with a nail?

ordinary nail (H4)

nail file
(H about 5)

steel file
(H about 6½)

Try scratching bottle glass with each of these three substances.

You can buy a small steel file, sandpaper, and emery paper in any hardware store.

Hardness Tests

Next to diamond, emery is the hardest mineral known. Emery is the name given to the mineral corundum when it is found mixed with iron impurities. The ruby and sapphire are also corundum.

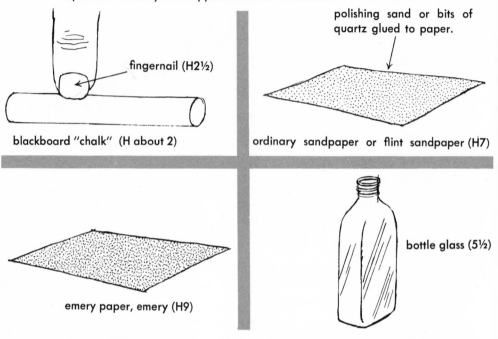

fingernail (H2½)

blackboard "chalk" (H about 2)

polishing sand or bits of quartz glued to paper.

ordinary sandpaper or flint sandpaper (H7)

emery paper, emery (H9)

bottle glass (5½)

Try scratching bottle glass, a nail file and a steel file with sandpaper and then with emery paper.

Leaving a mark is *not* the same as making a scratch or groove. Always rub the mark to make sure that what you see is really a scratch rather than a streak of powder.

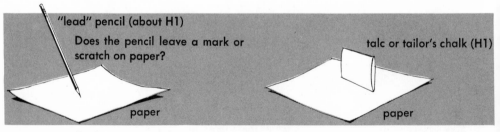

"lead" pencil (about H1)

Does the pencil leave a mark or scratch on paper?

paper

talc or tailor's chalk (H1)

paper

Minerals under H2½ will leave a mark on paper.
Does talc *scratch* the paper? Try scratching talc with edge of a card.
Remember, a true scratch cannot be rubbed off.

Acid Test

The acid test is used to find out whether or not a rock contains certain minerals called carbonates. If a rock fizzes or bubbles when a weak acid is put on it, then it is a carbonate rock. Limestone, marble, and chalk are examples of rocks rich in carbonates.

You will test for carbonates with ordinary household vinegar, a weak acid. If the rocks or shells or other substances contain carbonates, you will notice fizzing or bubbling. The fizzing is caused by tiny bubbles of a gas called carbon dioxide. The carbon dioxide is given up by carbonates when in contact with acid.

If a rock does not fizz when you add vinegar to it, then you know that it is not a carbonate rock. In doubtful cases it helps to powder a little of the rock by scraping the surface with a knife blade. A few drops of vinegar are then added to the small heap of powdered rock.

Acid Test

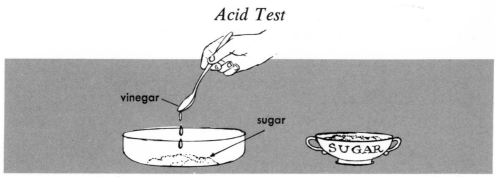

vinegar

sugar

SUGAR

Try the test on sugar. Is sugar a carbonate? Does it fizz?

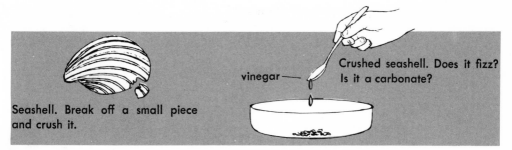

Seashell. Break off a small piece and crush it.

vinegar

Crushed seashell. Does it fizz? Is it a carbonate?

Acid Test

Certain minerals, called carbonates, fizz when acid touches them. The fizz is caused by a gas, carbon dioxide, which is given off by the minerals. Minerals that give off carbon dioxide are called carbonates. Baking soda is a man-made carbonate.

Vinegar contains a weak acid.

vinegar

Baking soda fizzes when a few drops of vinegar are added.

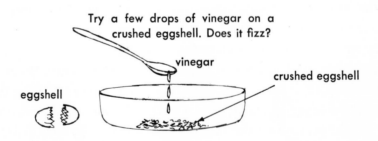

Try a few drops of vinegar on a crushed eggshell. Does it fizz?

vinegar

eggshell

crushed eggshell

vinegar

salt

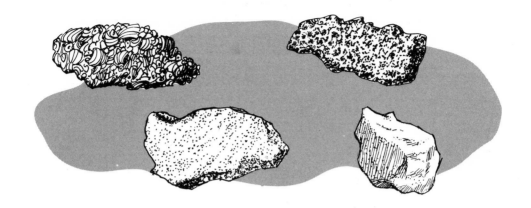

Limestone

One of our most useful kinds of rocks is between 3 and 4 in hardness. It is called limestone. Whole hillsides of limestone are sawed into blocks to make the foundations, walls, and floors of buildings.

The limestone we use today was once the shells of tiny sea animals. The seas they lived in covered large parts of our country. When the little animals died, their shells sank to the bottom of the sea. During thousands of years the layer of shells grew thicker. As more shells drifted down their weight pressed on the shells below. Finally the seas dried up. The water dried out of the pressed-down shells and they became the rock we call limestone. Pure limestone is the same as the scientist's chemical called "calcium carbonate." The mineral *calcite* is calcium carbonate in the form of crystals. Pure limestone has only one mineral in it — calcite.

If you look at a piece of limestone through a reading glass you will see tiny grains. If you put a few drops of acid on limestone, the rock will bubble.

Limestone

Nearly pure limestone has a hardness of 3 (H3). It is mainly calcium carbonate. Other minerals caught in it may make limestone slightly harder. All limestone can be scratched easily by a knife. Limestone dissolves slowly in ordinary water. It dissolves faster in water containing acid. Soda water is slightly acid. Soil often contains this acid, called carbonic acid. Rainwater containing this acid digs out tunnels and caves by dissolving underground limestone.

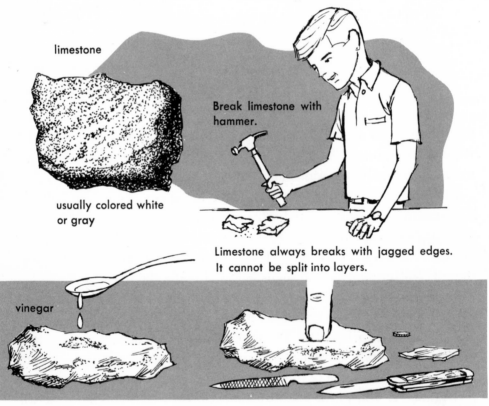

limestone

usually colored white or gray

Break limestone with hammer.

Limestone always breaks with jagged edges. It cannot be split into layers.

vinegar

Scrape limestone with file to form mound of powder. Limestone will fizz with vinegar.

Try scratching limestone with fingernail (H2½), with copper coin (H3), with a nail file (H5), with a knife blade (H5½), or with a piece of glass (H5½).

Limestone

no bubbles

Try this: limestone in cold, boiled water (limestone on bottom of dish)

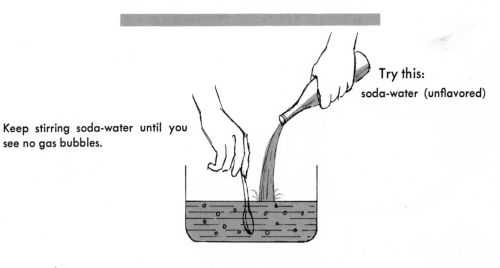

Keep stirring soda-water until you see no gas bubbles.

Try this: soda-water (unflavored)

Add a piece of limestone to your clear soda-water. Now wait about ten minutes. Do you see tiny gas bubbles on the limestone?

(Try this experiment with crushed eggshell if you have no limestone.)

Finely ground limestone is sold in gardening stores. You will need only a few cents' worth.

Limestone

Chalk is soft limestone made of the shells of tiny animals, too small to be seen without a microscope. Blackboard "chalk" has little or no real chalk in it. It is mainly a harder mineral called gypsum.

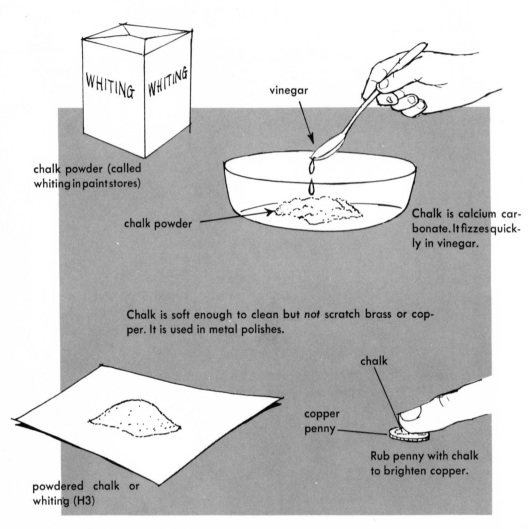

chalk powder (called whiting in paint stores)

chalk powder

vinegar

Chalk is calcium carbonate. It fizzes quickly in vinegar.

Chalk is soft enough to clean but *not* scratch brass or copper. It is used in metal polishes.

chalk

copper penny

Rub penny with chalk to brighten copper.

powdered chalk or whiting (H3)

You can buy a few cents' worth of whiting (powdered chalk) in any paint store.

Marble

Some limestone in the ground was squeezed for a long time. Heat inside the earth kept the rock very hot. This hot, pressed limestone slowly turned into marble.

Pure marble is white. Pink and red marble has iron in it. Black or green marble gets its color from other things pressed into the rock.

Marble can be cut or carved without cracking. It is polished to a beautiful shine and used for statues and buildings. The hardness of marble is 3. Because it is made of limestone, marble bubbles when drops of acid touch it.

Marble

The hardness of marble is 3 (H3). Marble cuts easily in all directions. Study a broken piece of marble. In coarse or low-grade marble the broken side is lumpy. In the finest marble the broken side seems soft, velvety. The size of the calcite crystals (calcium carbonate) makes the difference.

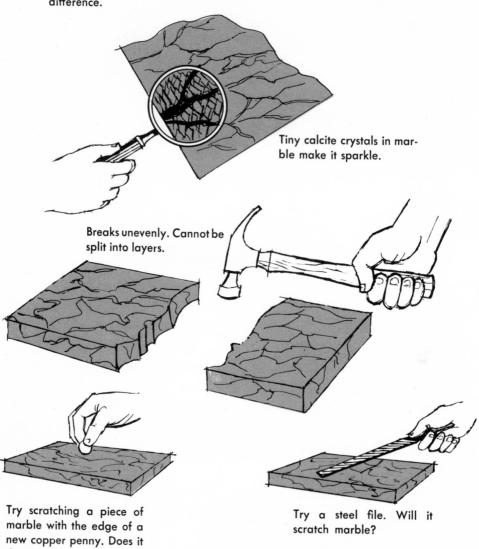

Tiny calcite crystals in marble make it sparkle.

Breaks unevenly. Cannot be split into layers.

Try scratching a piece of marble with the edge of a new copper penny. Does it dig a groove? Try scratching a penny with the edge of a piece of marble.

Try a steel file. Will it scratch marble?

You can get small pieces of marble at monument works, store-fixture shops, or building-supplies yards.

Marble

Carbon or graphite in marble causes black streaks.
Iron colors marble red or pink.
Chlorite makes marble green.

If your marble is not pure (because other minerals were caught in this rock), knots or wavy veins will show in the smooth marble.

Scrape some marble dust together with a file. Add a few drops of vinegar. Does it fizz? Does marble contain carbonates?

Rub the rough side of a piece of broken marble on ordinary sandpaper (H7).

Now try emery paper (H9). Which smoothes and polishes the marble faster?

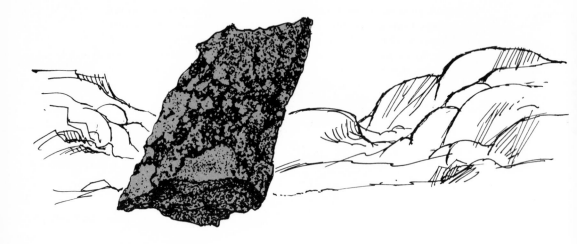

Granite

Granite is a light-colored, strong, and beautiful rock. Throughout granite are tiny grains that sparkle in the light. These are crystals of a mineral called feldspar. Mixed with the feldspar particles are grains of about equal size, with a glassy shine, called quartz. Granite always contains grains of feldspar and quartz along with one or more other minerals. You have seen the polished granite rock used in fine buildings and at the bottom of statues. If you look closely, you will see the grains of feldspar and quartz in the granite.

Most of the land of the world has granite beneath it. Mountains rest on granite. Many mountains have granite inside of them. When the soil on the top of mountains is worn away by years of rain and wind, you can see the granite of the mountains.

Granite is slowly worn down by weather and falls apart. As granite is worn down, the quartz in it crumbles into tiny sharp-edged grains we know as sand. The sand builders use is made up mainly of these tiny quartz grains.

Granite

Granite is a coarse-grained rock that is light in weight compared to most other rocks. It always contains, besides feldspar and quartz, either mica or hornblende or both. The mica may be either silvery-white or black. If the mica flakes are large enough, you can split off thin sheets or layers with a knife. Hornblende takes the form of long slender six-sided crystals usually of a greenish-black, black, or dark-brown color.

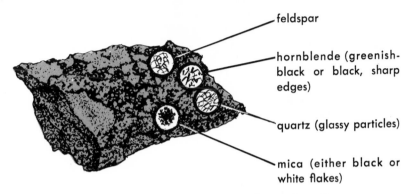

feldspar

hornblende (greenish-black or black, sharp edges)

quartz (glassy particles)

mica (either black or white flakes)

The minerals in granite can be seen without a magnifying glass. Can you point out the flakes of mica? Try to peel off a thin slice with a knife. Try to scratch flakes of mica with fingernail (H2½). Try to scratch flakes of mica with edge of penny (H3).

The steel file (H6½) will scratch the mica and feldspar easily and just about scratch the harder quartz particles, too.

Try to scratch the granite with a steel file.

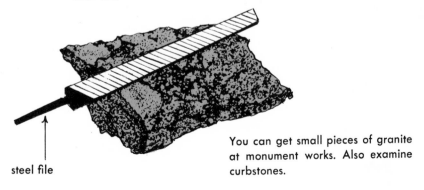

steel file

You can get small pieces of granite at monument works. Also examine curbstones.

Granite

How can you recognize Granite?

- It does not fizz in acid.
- It has a light color.
- It consists of tiny grains of at least two different minerals.
- Its minerals are easily seen without a reading glass. The quartz grains are glassy. The feldspar grains are gray or white or reddish. The mica crystals are white or colorless or black, with a pearly luster.
- It is light in weight compared with most other rocks.
- It looks "grainy."

vinegar

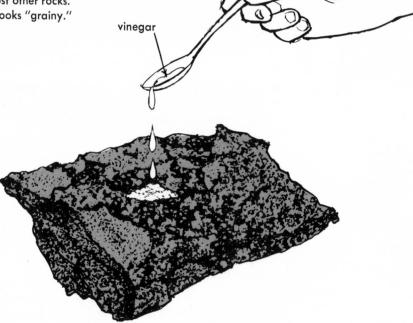

Scratch granite with steel file to collect some powder. Add a few drops of vinegar to the powdered granite. Does it fizz?

Granite

Pink granite contains pink or red feldspar.
Gray granite contains white or gray feldspar.
The "pudding" granite of Vermont contains lumps of black mica.

Try smoothing and polishing a rough piece of granite by rubbing it on coarse emery paper (H9). Does the color of the granite become clearer? Polishing this rough granite may take a half-hour. Moisten rock. Rub in a circle. Finish by rubbing on finer emery paper.

piece of granite

emery paper

Suggestion: If you live in a city, examine the curbstones. Are they made of granite?

Look at builder's sand through a reading glass.

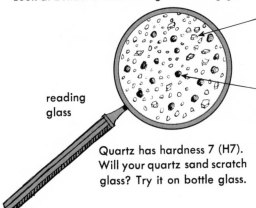

reading glass

Quartz has hardness 7 (H7). Will your quartz sand scratch glass? Try it on bottle glass.

The tiny grains are bits of quartz. Notice that they are almost transparent and have sharp edges. Beach sands, however, are always rounded.

The tiny pebbles are darker. They are *not* pure quartz. They usually contain quartz and other substances. They usually have rounded corners because of banging against other stones while rolling down streams.

You can rub off some of the sand from ordinary sandpaper. Notice how sharp-edged these bits of quartz are.

sandpaper

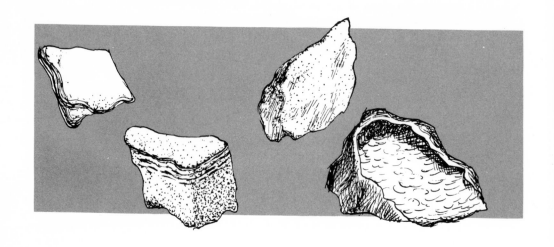

Sandstone

Sandstone is another rock that is carved and used in building. It is made of grains of quartz sand. The grains were held together until the sand became rock. Even though sandstone is solid rock, you can always see the separate grains of sand if you look carefully.

Different things may make the sand in sandstone stick together. If something called *silica* holds the grains of sand together, the sandstone is very strong. If lime holds the sand together, the sandstone is weak and crumbly.

You can dig between the grains of weak sandstone with your fingernails, or crumble the rock back into sand between your fingers.

Sandstone

Sandstone is made of grains of quartz sand cemented together. The color of sandstone depends on what is in the cement. Iron in the cement makes the sandstone red, yellow or brown.

Break a piece of sandstone with a hammer.

Can you see the grains of sand on the broken side? Cement holds the grains of sand together.

Sandstone is porous. This means the spaces between the sand grains are filled with air. When placed in water, bubbles of air are forced out.

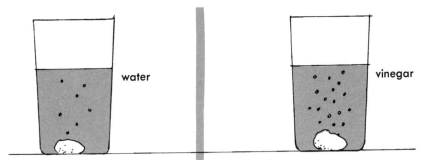

water

vinegar

Drop a piece of sandstone into water. Do you see bubbles of air rising?

Underground, sandstone can hold large amounts of water.

Drop another piece of sandstone into vinegar. Are there more bubbles this time? Do they keep rising for a longer time? If you see many bubbles these are carbon dioxide bubbles from the limy cement.

Allow to stand overnight. Examine each the next day.

Sandstone

Sandstone that can be split into slabs a few inches thick is called flagstone.* If often contains mica.

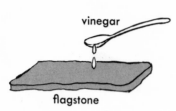

vinegar

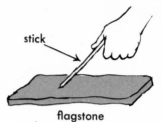

stick

flagstone

flagstone

Can you see grains of mica? Does the cement in it fizz with vinegar?

Some sandstone can be scratched with a copper penny or a stick. Notice that the scratch is on the soft cement and not on the grains of quartz sand (H7).

Make your own soft sandstone:

 ⅕ tbs.

"whiting" or powdered chalk

+

1 tbs.

fine sharp sand

and then mix by rolling together on a sheet of paper.

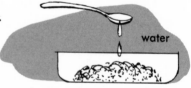

water

mixture of sand and chalk

Now add water and stir until mixture is like paste.

then

Pat into a small cube. Set aside to harden until next day.

Test your sandstone: Try to crumble a piece of it. Try to dissolve chalky cement by adding vinegar. Does the vinegar "work" on the sand, too?

*You can obtain a small piece of flagstone at a building-supplies yard.

Gypsum

Plaster walls in houses are often made of the rock called gypsum. Gypsum is heated until it becomes a white powder called *plaster of Paris*. Then water is added to the powder and it becomes the paste we call plaster. When plaster hardens, it turns back into gypsum rock again.

When you find rock gypsum in the ground, it may be white, gray, yellow, or red. Since its hardness is 2, you can scratch the rock with your fingernail.

There is a great deal of gypsum in our country. It was left behind by seas which once covered one-third of our land. The seas dried up, and the gypsum and salt from the water were left on dry land. In some parts of the U. S., the "rock gypsum," as it is called, is as thick as your school building is tall.

Gypsum

How plaster of Paris is made

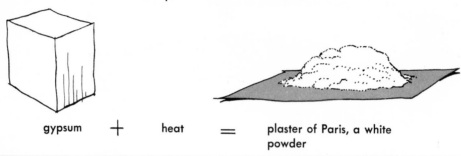

gypsum   +   heat   =   plaster of Paris, a white powder

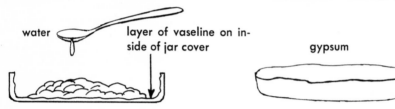

water · layer of vaseline on in-side of jar cover · gypsum

Mix plaster of Paris powder with about half as much water. Stir to a smooth, thick paste. Fill small container or metal jar-top with mixture.

Wait ½ hour for plaster of Paris to "set" and harden. You now have *gypsum* again. It "formed" when plaster of Paris absorbed water.

Can you scratch the gypsum with your fingernail?

Try scratching school "chalk" with your fingernail (H2½). School chalk is mainly gypsum.

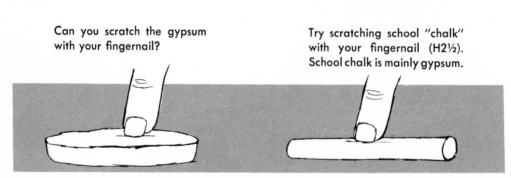

Notice that the plaster of Paris becomes warm for a time as it hardens or "sets." During this time it is absorbing water and turning back into gypsum. Gypsum has a hardness of 2.

Buy plaster of Paris at paint-supplies or hardware stores.

Gypsum

Gypsum will dissolve and fizz in strong acids. When a weak acid like vinegar is used, there is little or no fizzing.

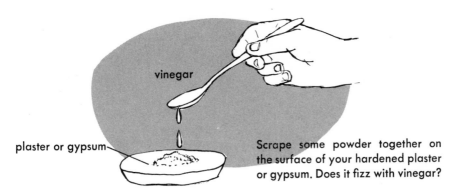

vinegar

plaster or gypsum

Scrape some powder together on the surface of your hardened plaster or gypsum. Does it fizz with vinegar?

You can make an imprint of a coin or medal in this way:

Rub some soap jelly (see page 48) on a coin and then push it into the wet plaster of Paris. Press down on coin lightly with finger for a few minutes. *After* the plaster has hardened or "set," remove coin and see mold or imprint.

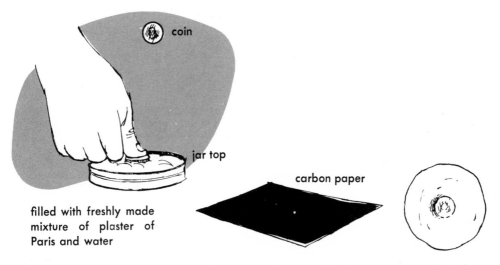

coin

jar top

carbon paper

filled with freshly made mixture of plaster of Paris and water

Rub imprint with piece of carbon paper to make it clearer.

Salt

Salt is one of the important minerals left behind by seas of long ago. Our bodies need salt. Salt is used in making soap. From salt comes a chemical called *chlorine*, which is used to make our water pure.

When you pour salt in a glass of water, it disappears. You know it is still there because you can taste it in the water. Scientists say that the salt has *dissolved*. When salty water dries up, as the seas in this country once did, the salt can be seen again. The small pieces of salt are called *crystals*.

We get our salt from mines in places which were once covered by salty seas. In some mines there is 300 feet of solid salt below the ground. Salt miners send hot water through tubes deep into the ground. Salt dissolves in the hot water. Pumps bring the salty water to pans on top of the ground. As the water in the pans dry up, the salt is left again in crystals.

Salt

How to make rock salt crystals

jar cover

clear salt water

salt at bottom

Half-fill a metal jar-cover with soil from your garden. To a glass of water, add and stir several teaspoons of salt, stopping when salt still remains at bottom even after long stirring. Pour some of the *clear* salt water on the soil. Put this mud-like mixture in the sun to dry, or set aside in a warm place. A loop of copper wire now placed on the mud will cause a necklace of crystals to form on it. After mud dries, large crystals, or rock salt, will also be seen on the mud.

Salt

Try scratching a large rock salt crystal with your fingernail (H2½). Try the edge of a copper penny (H3). What happens?

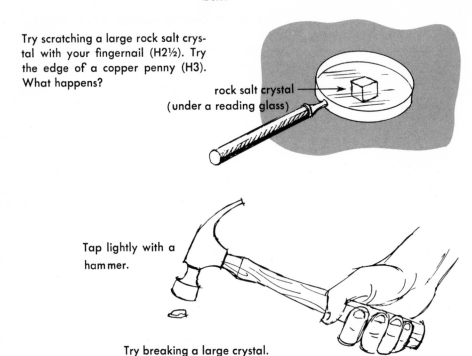

rock salt crystal
(under a reading glass)

Tap lightly with a hammer.

Try breaking a large crystal.

Does it break into small cubes? Notice how the crystal splits. Keep tapping and splitting until you get a few perfect cubes.

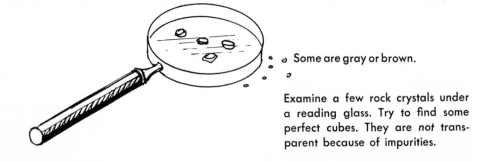

Some are gray or brown.

Examine a few rock crystals under a reading glass. Try to find some perfect cubes. They are *not* transparent because of impurities.

Salt

Table salt is the mineral halite. Its chemical name is sodium chloride. The hardness of salt is 2½.

Most salt is colorless to white. Impurities may make it gray, yellow or red. The salt left when the seas dried up is called rock salt. It is used to melt ice.

salt

water

Add a heaping tablespoon of salt to a glass of water. Stir until the salt dissolves. Taste the water.

1293162

Try this:

salt water

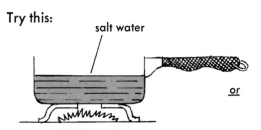

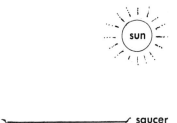

sun

<u>or</u>

saucer

Warm over a low flame to drive off the water. Do not boil. See tiny salt crystals left at bottom of pan.

Leave salt water in sun or in warm place for a few days. The salt crystals will be larger this time.

Sometimes sides are pushed in.

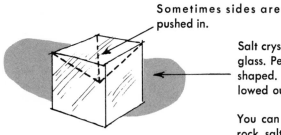

Salt crystal as seen through reading glass. Perfect salt crystals are cube-shaped. Some have their sides hollowed out.

You can buy a few cents' worth of rock salt, used for melting ice, at your grocer's.

Iron

Men discovered iron after they had been using copper for a long time. They melted iron from its ore, and began to use it for tools and spearheads. They found iron stronger than copper. They discovered that there is far more iron than copper in the earth.

In the United States, much iron ore is found in Michigan, Minnesota, and Wisconsin. This ore is heated in special furnaces to get the iron out of it. When some of the impurities are taken out of iron, it becomes steel.

Iron rusts and crumbles when it is left in the air. That is why the iron used in bridges and railings is always covered with paint.

Iron

Which is harder — an ordinary nail or glass?

Try to scratch bottle glass (5½) with a nail.

Now try a steel file. Does it scratch the glass?

Ordinary nails are made of soft steel, hardness 4 or 4½.

A steel file has a hardness of about 6½.

A nail, being "soft," can be bent without breaking.

A steel file will often break if used to pry things. Why?

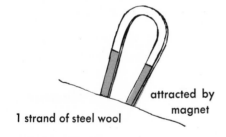

1 strand of steel wool

attracted by magnet

Roll steel wool together tightly. Bring it to magnet. Is it attracted?

When iron rusts it unites with the oxygen of the air. It then stops being attracted by a magnet.

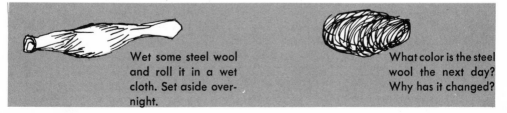

Wet some steel wool and roll it in a wet cloth. Set aside overnight.

What color is the steel wool the next day? Why has it changed?

Iron

Iron rusts in the air only when moisture is present. Acids speed up rusting. The baking-soda water is alkaline, the opposite of acid. It slows down rusting.

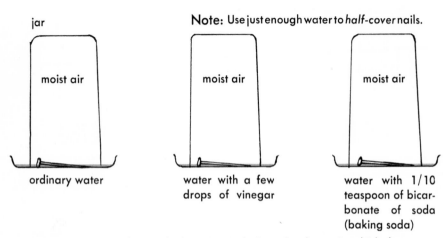

jar

Note: Use just enough water to *half-cover* nails.

moist air

moist air

moist air

ordinary water

water with a few drops of vinegar

water with 1/10 teaspoon of bicarbonate of soda (baking soda)

Place a clean nail in each glass. Set aside for a few hours. In which does the nail rust fastest? In which does it rust hardly at all?

Hydrogen is the lightest gas in the world. All acids contain hydrogen.

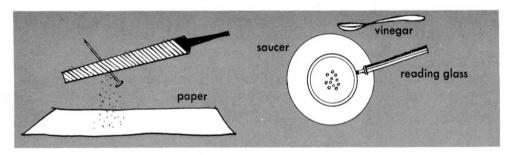

vinegar

saucer

reading glass

paper

File an ordinary nail. The tiny bits of iron that gather on the paper underneath are called iron filings. Keep at it until you have a small heap of filings.

Place the iron filings in a white saucer. Add 2 drops of vinegar. Wait 10 minutes. Study through a reading glass. Do you see small gas bubbles in the drop? These are hydrogen bubbles. The hydrogen comes from the acid in the vinegar.

Iron

Add a few drops of vinegar to a glass of water. Push some steel wool into the glass.

In a few hours some of the steel wool will rust through. The vinegar speeds up the rusting.

Try leaving steel wool in soapy water overnight.

Does it rust? Remember that soap is alkaline — *not* acid.

partly rusted steel wool

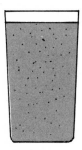

brown bits of rust left in the water

Place magnet in the water near the rust particles.

Pour some of the brown water into a saucer. You will see tiny rust particles. They are not attracted by a magnet. You may see a few bits of unchanged steel wool drawn quickly to the ends of the magnet.

Portland Cement

Men can make their own rock. They do it when strong stone of a special size and shape is needed. The man-made rock is called *concrete*. It is poured into wooden molds that have been built where the stone is needed — perhaps for a foundation. When concrete hardens, it becomes strong rock, able to hold up a heavy building or bridge.

Here's how concrete is made. It starts as a gray powder called *Portland cement*, which is a mixture of powdered limestone and clay. The mixture is heated in a special furnace until it becomes lumpy. Then the lumps are ground into powder and some powdered gypsum is added.

To make concrete from the Portland cement, men mix it with sand, gravel or crushed rock, and water. Then they quickly pour the concrete mixture into molds, where it hardens into rock.

Portland Cement

Buy a few pounds of Portland cement at a hardware store.

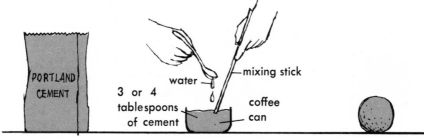

3 or 4 tablespoons of cement — Add water and mix until you get a thick paste.

Roll cement mixture into a ball. Set aside until the next day.

Test cement ball for strength by pressing it together with your fingers. Does it crumble? Why?

Now make a mixture called a *cement mortar* which will be strong enough to hold bricks or large stones together. Mix in a wooden box or in a can:

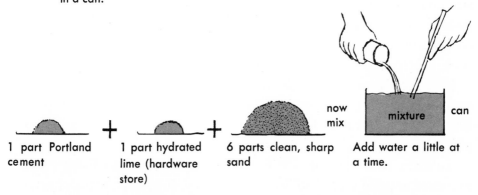

1 part Portland cement + 1 part hydrated lime (hardware store) + 6 parts clean, sharp sand — now mix — Add water a little at a time.

First mix the 3 substances dry by rolling back-and-forth many times on a newspaper. Then place dry mixture in a coffee can. Add water slowly. Keep mixing with stick. When "mix" becomes like paste stop adding water. Do *not* add too much water.

Remember: During and after your Portland cement experiments put the waste in a garbage can — *not* in the kitchen sink, where it will clog the drain.

Portland Cement

The materials in Portland cement unite with water to form a new hard substance. The crystals of this new substance hold the sand and pieces of stone together in the concrete or man-made stone.

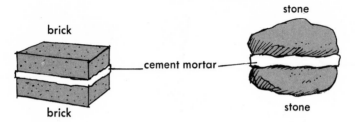

Wet two bricks. Put your cement mortar between them. Tap upper brick gently. Set aside for a few days to harden. Try same with the two flat stones.

How to make a concrete slab:

Mix

1 part cement

+

2 parts sharp clean sand

Then add

3 parts clean pebbles

Now mix all three together by rolling on newspaper as before. Place dry mixture in an old pan or pail.

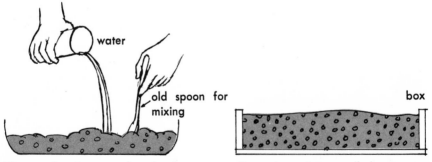

water

old spoon for mixing

box

Mixture of cement, sand and pebbles. Add water to mixture a little at a time and keep mixing until "pasty."

Pour your mixture called concrete into a wooden box. Set it aside to harden. Remove from box after a few days. Is the concrete slab hard?

Remember: *Put waste in garbage can.*

Aluminum

There is even more aluminum than iron in the earth. Aluminum can be found in most of the world's important rocks, but it is very hard to separate aluminum from its ores. In 1886, Charles M. Hall, an American scientist, found an inexpensive way of getting pure aluminum out of its ores. Today we have aluminum pots and pans, airplanes, paints, and even thin aluminum wrappings for chewing gum and candy bars.

Aluminum is very light. It weighs about one-third as much as steel. Aluminum does not rust or crumble when it is left in the air.

Aluminum

Aluminum is a soft metal. A small quantity of the metal manganese is added to the aluminum used in pots and pans. This makes the aluminum harder (about 2). Air causes a thin gray coating to form on aluminum. This protects the aluminum from air. Steel wool rubs this coating off. But soon it forms again in air.

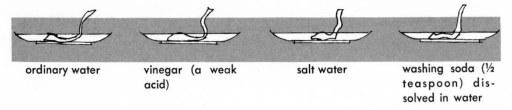

ordinary water   vinegar (a weak acid)   salt water   washing soda (½ teaspoon) dissolved in water

Bend strips of aluminum foil (from kitchen roll or candy wrappers) and set them in saucers containing different liquids as above. Let part of the aluminum stand up above the liquid. Does water change the aluminum? Vinegar? Salt water? Washing soda?

Note: Smooth out each strip with thumbnail.

Pure aluminum is not attacked by pure water. Salt corrodes or changes the surface — or outside — of aluminum. Alkalis, such as washing soda, also corrode aluminum. A weak acid like vinegar does not change aluminum noticeably. Most strong acids act on aluminum.

Try scratching aluminum pan with a copper penny (H3). Does it leave a groove? Try scratching the aluminum with a copper wire (H2½). Is the copper wire harder or softer than aluminum?

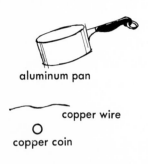

aluminum pan

copper wire

O
copper coin

steel wool (H about 5)

Rub a spot on aluminum pan with steel wool. Does the aluminum become brighter? Examine the part you rubbed about an hour later. Has it changed?

Water

Water is one of the most important substances men get from the earth. If we could dig deep enough, we would find water almost everywhere in the world.

You can see water going into the ground when it rains. After the rain stops, the water is still in the earth. It goes down deeper and deeper through tiny spaces in the soil and rocks. Finally the water is stopped by solid rock or clay. More and more water sinks through the earth. The top of the underground water is called the *water table*.

When men dig wells, they go deeper than the water table. Water fills the bottom of the well-hole slowly. Soon there is enough in the well to pump out. Sometimes there is no rain for a long time. Then the water table goes down and no water comes into the well-hole until it rains again. If a well is deep enough, it will not run dry very often.

Sometimes water from the water table comes out of an opening in the side of a hill. Where the water bubbles out of the hillside we see a spring. If the water table rises to the top of level ground we see a swamp. If it keeps on rising, the water forms a lake.

Water

salt

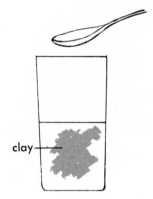

clay

Add a pinch of salt to water. Watch the grains of salt as they move towards the bottom. Stir slowly. Is the water clear? Can you see salt at the bottom of the glass?

Add a teaspoon of clay to water. Stir slowly. Is the water as clear this time? Does all the clay settle to the bottom?

Salt dissolves in water. We say it forms a solution. In a tightly closed bottle the dissolved salt in salt water will never settle.

Clay does *not* dissolve in water. Some clay particles settle quickly. Very tiny clay particles take weeks or months to get to the bottom of a closed bottle. We call clay in water a "suspension."

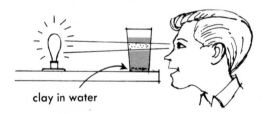

clay in water

Hold suspension of clay in water up to light bulb. Even after a few weeks the light will show the tiny clay particles still present in your suspension.

Two saucers, brown or green if possible, looking down:

Place a few drops of faucet water in dry saucer. Put aside until drop evaporates.

Try drop of rain water.

Examine the ring left by each drop under a reading glass. Which ring has more minerals in it?

Buy small package of fuller's earth (partly clay) in hardware store.

Water

As rain water soaks through the soil and runs over rocks it dissolves minerals. Sometimes these minerals prevent the water from forming suds with soap. We call this kind of water hard water. Fresh rain water is called soft water. It is pure and contains no minerals.

 or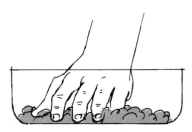

Add a tablespoon of hot water to a tablespoon of soap shavings. Stir to a thick jelly.

Squeeze soap and water with fingers to make a thick soap jelly.

Add 3 drops of soap jelly to a glass of rainwater. Place hand or cardboard over glass and shake. Do same with a glass of water from your faucet.

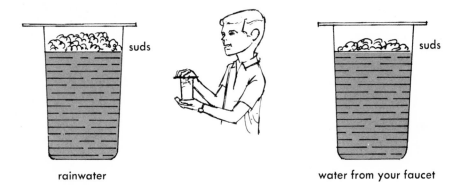

suds

rainwater

suds

water from your faucet

Which forms more suds? If hardly any soap suds form with your faucet water, what kind of water is it — hard or soft?

Water

The glass tube stands for a well. The water in the ground leaks into the well. After a heavy rain the level of the water table rises. Then the water in the well is nearer the top. In a dry season the water table may be so low that the well becomes "dry."

You can make a small model of a well to see how it works.

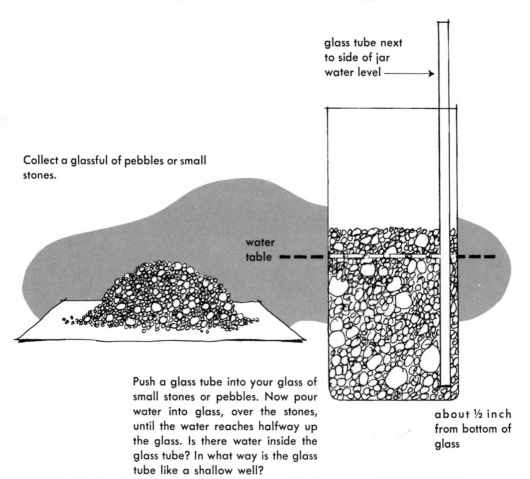

Collect a glassful of pebbles or small stones.

glass tube next to side of jar
water level ——→

water table - - -

about ½ inch from bottom of glass

Push a glass tube into your glass of small stones or pebbles. Now pour water into glass, over the stones, until the water reaches halfway up the glass. Is there water inside the glass tube? In what way is the glass tube like a shallow well?

You can buy a thick, short glass tube at a hardware store. Ask for the glass tube used in the water gauge of a furnace. You can also use the glass tube used for sipping liquids.

Soil

Most of the farming in the world is done in a layer of soil only about 12 inches thick. And it took thousands of years to make this thin layer.

Soil is made when water, ice, wind, and the sun's heat slowly break up the rocks on the top of the ground. Dead plants and animals mix with the crumbled rocks, making the soil darker and richer.

The top layer of dark soil is called *loam*. It is good soil for farming because it is made of tiny rock pieces, plant and animal remains, living plants and animals, air, and water.

Underneath the loam is *subsoil*. Subsoil is a lighter color than loam. It is made mostly of pieces of rock, and does not have enough plant and animal material for good farming.

Below the subsoil, there is crumbling rock. Under this layer is solid rock.

In places where there is much clay in the earth, the top layer of soil is called *heavy soil*. Heavy soil is not good for most farming because plant roots cannot go into it easily. Such heavy soil also takes longer to dry out after a rain.

Light soil is sandy soil. Plant roots go through it easily and it does not stay muddy long after rains.

Soil

Soil is made up of clay, sand, humus, water and air. Loam is any soil that will grow good crops. The brown or red or yellow color of soil is due to iron oxides. The black color is due to decayed vegetable matter which is dark gray or black. This is called humus.

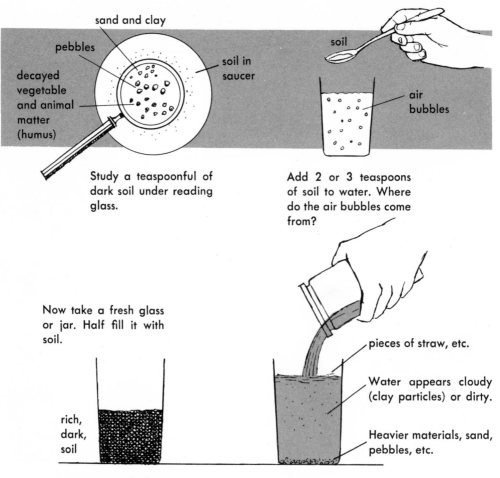

pebbles

sand and clay

soil in saucer

decayed vegetable and animal matter (humus)

soil

air bubbles

Study a teaspoonful of dark soil under reading glass.

Add 2 or 3 teaspoons of soil to water. Where do the air bubbles come from?

Now take a fresh glass or jar. Half fill it with soil.

pieces of straw, etc.

Water appears cloudy (clay particles) or dirty.

rich, dark, soil

Heavier materials, sand, pebbles, etc.

Add water up to about 1 inch from top. Stir and then let stand for a few minutes.

Why do clay particles take so long to settle? Why does the sand sink to the bottom quickly?

Soil

Clay particles are very tiny. They are less than .0001 of an inch in diameter. All clays are formed by the breaking down of rocks, especially feldspars, into a fine powder. Wind, water, ice, sun, and air act to break down or "weather" rocks.

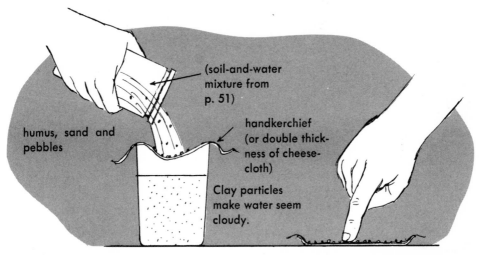

(soil-and-water mixture from p. 51)

humus, sand and pebbles

handkerchief (or double thickness of cheesecloth)

Clay particles make water seem cloudy.

Now pour your soil-and-water mixture through thin cotton cloth into a clean glass. Humus, sand, and pebbles will not pass through cloth.

Rub some of the material *left on* the cloth against a dry saucer. Does it feel gritty or scratchy? Why?

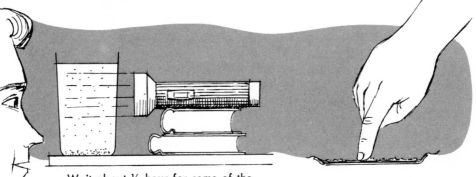

Wait about ½ hour for *some* of the clay particles to settle to bottom. Now look through liquid at flashlight bulb, or bare electric light bulb. Why does the light look yellow through liquid? Try looking at bulb through fresh, clean water. Is there a difference?

Now pour off liquid part. Try rubbing some of the clay from *bottom of glass* against a dry saucer. Is it scratchy? How does moist clay feel when rubbed between fingers?

51

Soil

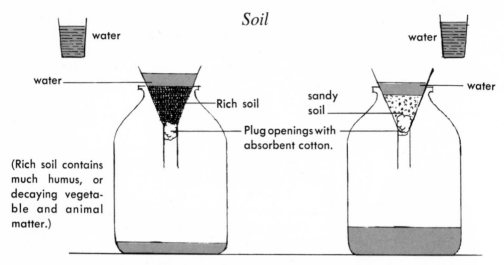

water

Rich soil

water

(Rich soil contains much humus, or decaying vegetable and animal matter.)

sandy soil

water

Plug openings with absorbent cotton.

Half-fill a funnel with rich dark soil. Half-fill another funnel with sand or sandy soil. Add same amount of water to each funnel. Through which does the water run faster? Why?

In the country, streams sometimes pour clay-bearing water into ponds or lakes. It may take days or even weeks for the clay to settle. In salt water, clay particles form clumps or balls which sink to the bottom quickly, leaving the water clear.

Take two glasses. Fill each with water. Add a teaspoon of salt to the water in *one* glass and stir.

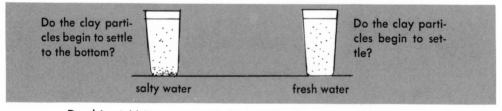

Do the clay particles begin to settle to the bottom?

Do the clay particles begin to settle?

salty water

fresh water

Do this: Add ¼ teaspoon of clay powder from your cloth in the previous experiment to each glass. Stir. Let stand for one hour. Examine and then let stand overnight. In which glass does the clay sink to bottom faster? Why?

If your soil in experiment on page 51 gave you very little clay, use a teaspoon of either fuller's earth or fire-clay for this experiment. Get a half-pound of one of these at your hardware store.

Further Reading

Try your school or public library for the books listed below. Some are elementary and easy to read; others are more advanced, more thorough. Be sure to examine both kinds. If a book seems simple to you, then go on to a more difficult one. This is an excellent way of learning more and more, by yourself, about any subject that interests you. If your library does not have the books mentioned here, then try other books on rocks and minerals. Some of these may be just as good as the ones recommended on this page.

Cormack, Maribelle B., *The First Book of Stones*, Watts, 1950.
Fenton, C. L. and Fenton, M. B., *The Rock Book*, Doubleday, 1940.
Fenton, C. L. and Fenton, M. B., *Riches from the Earth*, Day, 1953.
Loomis, Frederick B., *Field Book of Common Rocks and Minerals*, Putnam, 1948.
Pearl, Richard M., *How to Know the Minerals and Rocks*, New American Library (paperbound), 1957.
Shuttlesworth, Dorothy, *First Guide to Rocks*, Doubleday, 1963.
White, Anne T., *All about Our Changing Rocks*, Random, 1955.
Zim, Herbert S. and Paul R. Shaffer, *Rocks and Minerals*, Golden, 1957.

Often a good encyclopedia will offer more facts and details about a particular rock or mineral than will be found in a book. Use the index volume of an encyclopedia to look up a particular rock or mineral. Then read the article slowly, two or three times, so as to get as much as possible out of it. You will find this method rewarding.

The following encyclopedias may prove useful to you:

The Book of Knowledge: The Children's Encyclopedia
Britannica Junior
Compton's Pictured Encyclopedia and Fact Index
The World Book Encyclopedia

Index

Glossary

CHALK — A soft limestone, white or gray or buff in color, composed of the tiny shells of one-celled animals.

CHLORITE — A group of silicate minerals; the name chlorite comes from the Greek word meaning "green"; the presence of chlorite in marble and many other rocks gives them their greenish color; although they look like mica, sheets of chlorite will *not* spring back after being bent.

CLAY — A soft rock composed of particles smaller than 0.0001 inch; clay feels soft and oily, but becomes slippery and plastic when wet.

CONCRETE — An artificial building material made by mixing Portland cement and sand with gravel or broken stones and water; the cement soon "sets" and binds the entire mass, thus forming the hard, strong material called concrete.

EMERY — A granular material used for grinding because it is harder than any common mineral; emery powder is a mixture of corundum or aluminum oxide and magnetite or black iron oxide.

GRAPHITE — A non-metallic mineral, very soft, and greasy to the touch; it consists entirely of carbon and is used in "lead" pencils and for lubricating machinery.

GYPSUM — A white or gray mineral consisting of calcium sulphate; it is used to make plaster of Paris and wallboard; common school "chalk" is mainly gypsum.

HALITE — The mineral name for table salt or sodium chloride; it occurs in cube-shaped crystals; though usually transparent, it may also be gray or yellow or red because of impurities.

HARDNESS — The ability of a smooth surface to resist being scratched.

LOAM — A dark soil that will grow good crops; it consists of a mixture of sand, clay, decayed vegetable and animal matter, and living plants and animals.

MICAS — A group of minerals with the unusual property of peeling into thin sheets; these thin and tough layers or sheets can be bent and will spring back when released.

MINERAL — Any natural inorganic substance, with every part of it the same, and with a definite chemical composition; it is generally solid and most often has a crystalline structure.

ORE — A rock or mineral from which metal can be profitably extracted.

ROCKS — Any large natural mass of material of which the earth is constructed; except for certain glassy forms, rocks contain one or more minerals.

RUST — A reddish coating formed on iron when it unites chemically with the oxygen of moist air.

SAND — Any mass of small rock particles; the sand used by builders consists largely of grains of quartz.

SANDSTONE — Any rock made up of grains of sand that are held together by cement.

SOIL — The loose surface material on which plants can grow; it is made up of small bits of rocks usually mixed with decayed plant and animal matter.

TALC — A pale-green or white mineral that feels soapy and can be scratched by a fingernail; small pieces are sometimes called French chalk or tailor's chalk; talc is one of the softest of minerals.

The Authors

Harry Sootin is a New Yorker who has taught general science and physics in the New York City high schools for over twenty-five years. A graduate of the City College of New York. Mr. Sootin began his career as a chemist, and soon switched to teaching. He was a member of the faculty of the High School of Commerce in Manhattan, and then taught at Flushing High School on Long Island. He has always favored the laboratory approach to science teaching, believing that it is most effective in interesting his students in scientific facts and ideas.

In addition to his teaching duties, Mr. Sootin has devoted much of his time to writing. He is the author of some eight books for young people, including biographies of Isaac Newton, Michael Faraday, Gregor Mendel, and Robert Boyle. Mr. Sootin has written many science articles for magazines, as well as for the *Book of Knowledge*. He is a member of the American Association for the Advancement of Science, the History of Science Society, and the Teachers Guild. He lives in Flushing, New York.

Laura Sootin is Harry Sootin's daughter. After graduating from Smith College, where she majored in English, Miss Sootin studied at the Bank Street College of Education in New York City. She has written for a number of children's magazines, and is the author of several books for young readers as well. She is married and lives with her husband and two children in Boston, Massachusetts.